Key Stage 2

Multiplication & Division

Hilary Koll and Steve Mills

Name _____

Schofield & Sims

Introduction

Understanding how multiplication and division work is as important as knowing when and how to use them. In this book you will learn and practise different ways to multiply and divide numbers using both mental and written methods. Trying each method will help you to build a better understanding of what is happening as you multiply and divide.

How to use this book

Before you start using this book, write your name in the name box on the first page.

Then decide how to begin. If you want a complete course on multiplication and division, you should work right through the book from beginning to end. Another way to use the book is to dip into it when you want to find out about a particular topic, such as scaling. The Contents page will help you to find the pages you need.

Whichever way you choose, don't try to do too much at once – it's better to work through the book in short bursts.

When you have found the topic you want to study, look out for these icons, which mark different parts of the text.

This icon shows you the activities that you should complete. You write your answers in the spaces provided. You might find it useful to have some spare paper to work on for some of the activities. After you have worked through all the activities on the page, turn to pages 61–66 at the end of the book to check your answers. When you are sure that you understand the topic, put a tick in the box beside it on the Contents page.

On pages 13, 24, 40 and 54 you will find **Progress tests**. These contain questions that will check your understanding of the topics that you have worked through so far. Check your answers on page 67. It is important that you correct any mistakes before moving on to the next section.

On pages 57–60 you will find a **Final test**. This will check your understanding of all the topics. Check your answers on page 68.

Explanation

This text explains the topic and gives examples. Make sure you read it before you start the activities.

This text gives you useful background information about the subject.

Contents

Multiplying

Explanation

Multiplication is just a quick way of adding lots of the same number.
Instead of adding **6 + 6 + 6 + 6 + 6** you can say 'five lots of six' or 'five times six'.

Use a multiplication sign (×) when you multiply numbers together. $5 \times 6 = 30$

Multiplication is the opposite of division, and division is the opposite of multiplication. If you multiply by a number and then divide by it, you are left with the number you started with.

Example $5 \times 6 \div 6 = 5$

Multiplication words

These words often mean **multiply**.

times	groups of	product

multiplied by	lots of	double

Did you know?

It **does not** matter which way round you do a multiplication question, as the answer will be the **same**.

$$4 \times 8 = 32$$
$$8 \times 4 = 32$$

Activities

1   Answer these questions.

a $4 \times 5 =$ _____ $5 \times 4 =$ _____

b $3 \times 7 =$ _____ $7 \times 3 =$ _____

c $2 \times 9 =$ _____ $9 \times 2 =$ _____

d $5 \times 3 =$ _____ $3 \times 5 =$ _____

e $10 \times 4 =$ _____ $4 \times 10 =$ _____

f $6 \times 10 =$ _____ $10 \times 6 =$ _____

g $4 \times 3 =$ _____ $3 \times 4 =$ _____

h $5 \times 2 =$ _____ $2 \times 5 =$ _____

Dividing

Explanation

Division is what happens when you share things equally or divide things into equal groups.

$$8 \div 2$$

Equal sharing

8 children get into 2 teams.
There are 4 in each team.

$$8 \div 2 = 4$$

Equal grouping

8 children get into teams of 2.
There are 4 teams.

$$8 \div 2 = 4$$

The answer is the same whichever method you use.

Use these signs to show division: ÷ and $\overline{)}$

$$12 \div 6 \qquad 6\overline{)12}$$

Division is the opposite of multiplication, and multiplication is the opposite of division. If you divide by a number and then multiply by it, you are left with the number you started with.

Example $12 \div 6 \times 6 = 12$

Division words

These words often mean **divide**:

share	equal groups of	split equally

divided by	shared between	halve

Did you know?

It **does** matter which way round you do a division question, as the answer will **not** be the same.

$$8 \div 4 = 2$$

$$4 \div 8 = \tfrac{1}{2}$$

Activities

1   Answer these questions.

a $8 \div 2 =$ _____   b $10 \div 2 =$ _____   c $12 \div 3 =$ _____   d $15 \div 5 =$ _____

e $16 \div 4 =$ _____   f $9 \div 3 =$ _____   g $10 \div 5 =$ _____   h $20 \div 2 =$ _____

Links between multiplication and division

Multiplying and dividing are closely related.
They are opposites, because one 'undoes' the other.
The mathematical term for this is 'inverse'.
Multiplication and division are **inverses**.

$$6 \times 3 = 18$$

$$18 \div 3 = 6$$

Activities

1 Follow the steps below to find the answer, like this:

$$2 \times 4 \div 2 \times 3 \div 4 \times 2 \div 3 = \underline{\qquad}$$

a | 2 | times **4** | divide by **2** | times **3** | divide by **4** | times **2** | divide by **3** | _____

b | 12 | divide by **3** | times **4** | divide by **2** | times **2** | divide by **4** | times **3** | _____

c | 5 | times **2** | divide by **5** | times **3** | divide by **2** | times **5** | divide by **3** | _____

d | 30 | divide by **10** | times **3** | divide by **3** | times **5** | divide by **5** | times **10** | _____

2 What do you notice about each of your answers? Why do you think this is?

_____

_____

_____

3 Use these multiplication and division facts to help you answer the questions below.

$5 \times 4 = 20$	$20 \div 10 = 2$	$4 \times 3 = 12$
$15 \div 3 = 5$	$10 \times 4 = 40$	$25 \div 5 = 5$

a $20 \div 5 = \underline{\qquad}$ **b** $40 \div 4 = \underline{\qquad}$ **c** $10 \times 2 = \underline{\qquad}$

d $5 \times 5 = \underline{\qquad}$ **e** $12 \div 3 = \underline{\qquad}$ **f** $5 \times 3 = \underline{\qquad}$

Learning your 2, 3, 4, 5 and 10 times tables

Explanation

You need to learn the facts below because they make doing multiplication questions easier.

× 2	× 3	× 4	× 5	× 10
$1 \times 2 = 2$	$1 \times 3 = 3$	$1 \times 4 = 4$	$1 \times 5 = 5$	$1 \times 10 = 10$
$2 \times 2 = 4$	$2 \times 3 = 6$	$2 \times 4 = 8$	$2 \times 5 = 10$	$2 \times 10 = 20$
$3 \times 2 = 6$	$3 \times 3 = 9$	$3 \times 4 = 12$	$3 \times 5 = 15$	$3 \times 10 = 30$
$4 \times 2 = 8$	$4 \times 3 = 12$	$4 \times 4 = 16$	$4 \times 5 = 20$	$4 \times 10 = 40$
$5 \times 2 = 10$	$5 \times 3 = 15$	$5 \times 4 = 20$	$5 \times 5 = 25$	$5 \times 10 = 50$
$6 \times 2 = 12$	$6 \times 3 = 18$	$6 \times 4 = 24$	$6 \times 5 = 30$	$6 \times 10 = 60$
$7 \times 2 = 14$	$7 \times 3 = 21$	$7 \times 4 = 28$	$7 \times 5 = 35$	$7 \times 10 = 70$
$8 \times 2 = 16$	$8 \times 3 = 24$	$8 \times 4 = 32$	$8 \times 5 = 40$	$8 \times 10 = 80$
$9 \times 2 = 18$	$9 \times 3 = 27$	$9 \times 4 = 36$	$9 \times 5 = 45$	$9 \times 10 = 90$
$10 \times 2 = 20$	$10 \times 3 = 30$	$10 \times 4 = 40$	$10 \times 5 = 50$	$10 \times 10 = 100$
$11 \times 2 = 22$	$11 \times 3 = 33$	$11 \times 4 = 44$	$11 \times 5 = 55$	$11 \times 10 = 110$
$12 \times 2 = 24$	$12 \times 3 = 36$	$12 \times 4 = 48$	$12 \times 5 = 60$	$12 \times 10 = 120$

Did you know?

When you learn a tables fact you get two for the price of one! If you know one fact you automatically know another. So, with each fact you learn, turn it around to get another.

Example $9 \times 4 = 36$ and $4 \times 9 = 36$

When you are sure that you know a fact in the tables above, tick it. Make sure you know its partner, and tick it too if it is in the tables above.

Activities

1 Cover the times tables above. Answer these questions.

a $5 \times 4 =$ _____   b $8 \times 5 =$ _____   c $7 \times 3 =$ _____   d $3 \times 5 =$ _____

e $9 \times 10 =$ _____   f $7 \times 4 =$ _____   g $5 \times 5 =$ _____   h $3 \times 4 =$ _____

i $5 \times 2 =$ _____   j $11 \times 3 =$ _____   k $2 \times 4 =$ _____   l $9 \times 4 =$ _____

m $4 \times 10 =$ _____   n $9 \times 2 =$ _____   o $12 \times 10 =$ _____   p $9 \times 5 =$ _____

q $6 \times 3 =$ _____   r $6 \times 4 =$ _____   s $6 \times 2 =$ _____   t $4 \times 4 =$ _____

u $12 \times 2 =$ _____   v $8 \times 3 =$ _____   w $7 \times 5 =$ _____   x $8 \times 2 =$ _____

Counting in multiples of 2, 3, 4, 5 and 10

Explanation

The answers to multiplication questions are called multiples. **3 × 5 = 15**, so **15** is a multiple of **3** and of **5**.

Multiples of a number can be created by counting on in equal steps from zero. The first **12** multiples of **3** are **3, 6, 9, 12, 15, 18, 21, 24, 27, 30, 33** and **36**.

Multiples continue beyond the times table, so other multiples of **3** include **39, 60, 300, 9000** and **12 000**.

Activities

1 Write the first **12** multiples of **5**.

2 Write the first **12** multiples of **10**.

3 What do you notice about the multiples of **5** and the multiples of **10**? (Look at the two rows together.)

_____

4 Write the first **12** multiples of **2**.

5 Write the first **12** multiples of **4**.

6 What do you notice about the multiples of **2** and the multiples of **4**?

_____

7 Can you use this information to write the multiples of **8** using the multiples of **4**?

Division facts 1

Explanation

The division facts below are linked to the **2**, **3**, **4**, **5** and **10** times tables. Try to learn them because they make doing division questions easier. Use the tables you know, such as **3 × 5 = 15** to help you answer related divisions, such as **15 ÷ 3 = 5** or **15 ÷ 5 = 3**.

÷ 2	÷ 3	÷ 4	÷ 5	÷ 10
2 ÷ 2 = 1	3 ÷ 3 = 1	4 ÷ 4 = 1	5 ÷ 5 = 1	10 ÷ 10 = 1
4 ÷ 2 = 2	6 ÷ 3 = 2	8 ÷ 4 = 2	10 ÷ 5 = 2	20 ÷ 10 = 2
6 ÷ 2 = 3	9 ÷ 3 = 3	12 ÷ 4 = 3	15 ÷ 5 = 3	30 ÷ 10 = 3
8 ÷ 2 = 4	12 ÷ 3 = 4	16 ÷ 4 = 4	20 ÷ 5 = 4	40 ÷ 10 = 4
10 ÷ 2 = 5	15 ÷ 3 = 5	20 ÷ 4 = 5	25 ÷ 5 = 5	50 ÷ 10 = 5
12 ÷ 2 = 6	18 ÷ 3 = 6	24 ÷ 4 = 6	30 ÷ 5 = 6	60 ÷ 10 = 6
14 ÷ 2 = 7	21 ÷ 3 = 7	28 ÷ 4 = 7	35 ÷ 5 = 7	70 ÷ 10 = 7
16 ÷ 2 = 8	24 ÷ 3 = 8	32 ÷ 4 = 8	40 ÷ 5 = 8	80 ÷ 10 = 8
18 ÷ 2 = 9	27 ÷ 3 = 9	36 ÷ 4 = 9	45 ÷ 5 = 9	90 ÷ 10 = 9
20 ÷ 2 = 10	30 ÷ 3 = 10	40 ÷ 4 = 10	50 ÷ 5 = 10	100 ÷ 10 = 10
22 ÷ 2 = 11	33 ÷ 3 = 11	44 ÷ 4 = 11	55 ÷ 5 = 11	110 ÷ 10 = 11
24 ÷ 2 = 12	36 ÷ 3 = 12	48 ÷ 4 = 12	60 ÷ 5 = 12	120 ÷ 10 = 12

Activities

1 Cover the division facts above and test yourself on these questions.

a 12 ÷ 3 = ____   b 22 ÷ 2 = ____   c 40 ÷ 5 = ____   d 30 ÷ 10 = ____

e 36 ÷ 4 = ____   f 45 ÷ 5 = ____   g 24 ÷ 3 = ____   h 16 ÷ 2 = ____

i 60 ÷ 10 = ____   j 36 ÷ 3 = ____   k 24 ÷ 2 = ____   l 44 ÷ 4 = ____

m 60 ÷ 5 = ____   n 32 ÷ 4 = ____   o 110 ÷ 10 = ____   p 18 ÷ 3 = ____

q 18 ÷ 2 = ____   r 70 ÷ 10 = ____   s 48 ÷ 4 = ____   t 35 ÷ 5 = ____

u 27 ÷ 3 = ____   v 14 ÷ 2 = ____   w 25 ÷ 5 = ____   x 28 ÷ 4 = ____

Multiplication and division words

Activities

1 Write each question as either a multiplication or a division question and then answer it.

a What is **3** times **4**? _____

b How many groups of **3** are in **9**? _____

c What is **7** multiplied by **5**? _____

d What is **18** shared between **3**? _____

e Find **4** groups of **10**. _____

f Share **120** by **10**. _____

g Divide **66** by **6**. _____

h How many teams of **4** are there in **24**? _____

i What is **50** split equally between **5**? _____

j What is the product of **4** and **11**? _____

k How many is **12** groups of **3**? _____

2 Write each question using multiplication or division words.

a $3 \times 5 =$ _____

b $45 \div 5 =$ _____

c $24 \div 4 =$ _____

Word problems

Activities

1 Answer these one-step word problems.

a James saves £8 each week for **10** weeks.
How much money does he save altogether? _____

b Hayley shares £**24** equally among her three daughters.
How much does each daughter get? _____

c There are two avocados in each pack.
How many avocados are there in five packs? _____

d **33** children get into teams of three. How many teams are there? _____

e Libby's pencils are all the same length. Each pencil is **12**cm long.
If she puts five of the pencils end-to-end, how long is the line? _____

f Leo runs **10**km every day for seven days. How far does he
run altogether? _____

g There are **35** children at a club. They are put into five equal teams.
How many children are in each team? _____

h Ahmad buys three tubes of sweets. There are nine sweets in
each tube. How many sweets does he have? _____

i Chloe has **36** grapes. She shares them equally among four friends.
How many grapes does each friend get? _____

Doubling and halving 1

Explanation

When you **double** a number you **multiply it by 2**.

These are different ways of saying 'double'.

times by 2	multiply by 2	twice

Doubling

To double a 2-digit number you can use partitioning, like this:

• partition the number into tens and units

• multiply each number by **2**

• add the two numbers together.

For more information on partitioning, see pages 25 and 28.

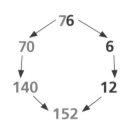

Activities

1 Double these numbers.

a 19 _____   b 23 _____   c 36 _____   d 42 _____   e 45 _____

f 48 _____   g 53 _____   h 68 _____   i 77 _____   j 89 _____

When you **halve** a number **you divide it by 2**. These are different ways of saying 'halve'.

divide by 2	half

Halving

You can also use partitioning to halve a 2- or 3-digit number, like this:

• partition the number

• divide each number by **2**

• add the two numbers together.

For more information on partitioning, see pages 25 and 28.

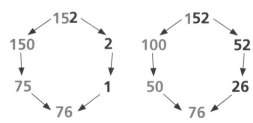

2 Halve these numbers.

a 62 _____   b 78 _____   c 84 _____   d 92 _____   e 98 _____

f 104 _____   g 126 _____   h 132 _____   i 168 _____   j 178 _____

Progress test 1

1 Follow the steps to find the answer.

| 4 | times **3** | divide by **2** | times **4** | divide by **4** | times **2** | divide by **3** | _____ |

2 Answer these multiplication questions.

a 3 × 7 = _____   b 5 × 4 = _____   c 3 × 4 = _____

d 11 × 10 = _____   e 6 × 3 = _____   f 5 × 5 = _____

g 12 × 2 = _____   h 9 × 4 = _____   i 12 × 5 = _____

3 Write the first **12** multiples of **3**.

4 Answer these division questions.

a 12 ÷ 4 = _____   b 18 ÷ 3 = _____   c 35 ÷ 5 = _____

d 100 ÷ 10 = _____   e 21 ÷ 3 = _____   f 24 ÷ 4 = _____

g 36 ÷ 4 = _____   h 24 ÷ 2 = _____   i 21 ÷ 3 = _____

5 Write each as a multiplication or division question and answer it.

a What is **7** multiplied by **5**?   _____

b What is **50** split equally between **10**?   _____

c What is the product of **4** and **7**?   _____

6 Answer these one-step word problems.

a Evie saves £**3** each week for nine weeks.
   How much money does she save?   _____

b Jane has **18** sweets that she shares equally among
   her three sons. How many does each son get?   _____

Learning your 6, 7, 8 and 9 times tables

You need to learn the facts below because they make doing multiplication questions easier.

× 6	× 7	× 8	× 9
1 × 6 = 6	1 × 7 = 7	1 × 8 = 8	1 × 9 = 9
2 × 6 = 12	2 × 7 = 14	2 × 8 = 16	2 × 9 = 18
3 × 6 = 18	3 × 7 = 21	3 × 8 = 24	3 × 9 = 27
4 × 6 = 24	4 × 7 = 28	4 × 8 = 32	4 × 9 = 36
5 × 6 = 30	5 × 7 = 35	5 × 8 = 40	5 × 9 = 45
6 × 6 = 36	6 × 7 = 42	6 × 8 = 48	6 × 9 = 54
7 × 6 = 42	7 × 7 = 49	7 × 8 = 56	7 × 9 = 63
8 × 6 = 48	8 × 7 = 56	8 × 8 = 64	8 × 9 = 72
9 × 6 = 54	9 × 7 = 63	9 × 8 = 72	9 × 9 = 81
10 × 6 = 60	10 × 7 = 70	10 × 8 = 80	10 × 9 = 90
11 × 6 = 66	11 × 7 = 77	11 × 8 = 88	11 × 9 = 99
12 × 6 = 72	12 × 7 = 84	12 × 8 = 96	12 × 9 = 108

Activities

1 Cover the tables above and test yourself on these questions.

a 5 × 6 = _____   b 8 × 7 = _____   c 7 × 7 = _____   d 3 × 6 = _____

e 9 × 10 = _____   f 6 × 8 = _____   g 8 × 8 = _____   h 7 × 9 = _____

i 5 × 8 = _____   j 11 × 6 = _____   k 4 × 7 = _____   l 7 × 8 = _____

m 9 × 9 = _____   n 7 × 6 = _____   o 12 × 9 = _____   p 6 × 6 = _____

q 3 × 8 = _____   r 8 × 6 = _____   s 9 × 8 = _____   t 5 × 9 = _____

u 12 × 8 = _____   v 8 × 9 = _____   w 10 × 7 = _____   x 9 × 7 = _____

2 Practise your tables with a pack of playing cards. Take out the picture cards and put the rest face down in a pile. Turn two cards over together and multiply the numbers. Keep the cards if you know the answer. Check any you're not sure of. How quickly can you work through the pile?

Did you know?

Some of these facts can be tricky but, remember, if you know one fact you automatically know another.   **9 × 8 = 72** and **8 × 9 = 72**

Division facts 2

Explanation

The division facts below are linked to your **6**, **7**, **8**, **9** and **10** times tables. Try to learn them because they make doing division questions easier.

÷ 6	÷ 7	÷ 8	÷ 9	÷ 10
$6 \div 6 = 1$	$7 \div 7 = 1$	$8 \div 8 = 1$	$9 \div 9 = 1$	$10 \div 10 = 1$
$12 \div 6 = 2$	$14 \div 7 = 2$	$16 \div 8 = 2$	$18 \div 9 = 2$	$20 \div 10 = 2$
$18 \div 6 = 3$	$21 \div 7 = 3$	$24 \div 8 = 3$	$27 \div 9 = 3$	$30 \div 10 = 3$
$24 \div 6 = 4$	$28 \div 7 = 4$	$32 \div 8 = 4$	$36 \div 9 = 4$	$40 \div 10 = 4$
$30 \div 6 = 5$	$35 \div 7 = 5$	$40 \div 8 = 5$	$45 \div 9 = 5$	$50 \div 10 = 5$
$36 \div 6 = 6$	$42 \div 7 = 6$	$48 \div 8 = 6$	$54 \div 9 = 6$	$60 \div 10 = 6$
$42 \div 6 = 7$	$49 \div 7 = 7$	$56 \div 8 = 7$	$63 \div 9 = 7$	$70 \div 10 = 7$
$48 \div 6 = 8$	$56 \div 7 = 8$	$64 \div 8 = 8$	$72 \div 9 = 8$	$80 \div 10 = 8$
$54 \div 6 = 9$	$63 \div 7 = 9$	$72 \div 8 = 9$	$81 \div 9 = 9$	$90 \div 10 = 9$
$60 \div 6 = 10$	$70 \div 7 = 10$	$80 \div 8 = 10$	$90 \div 9 = 10$	$100 \div 10 = 10$

Activities

1 Cover the facts above and test yourself on these questions.

a $42 \div 6 =$ _____   b $35 \div 7 =$ _____   c $40 \div 8 =$ _____   d $27 \div 9 =$ _____

e $36 \div 9 =$ _____   f $48 \div 8 =$ _____   g $42 \div 7 =$ _____   h $64 \div 8 =$ _____

i $32 \div 8 =$ _____   j $36 \div 6 =$ _____   k $45 \div 9 =$ _____   l $49 \div 7 =$ _____

m $54 \div 9 =$ _____   n $56 \div 7 =$ _____   o $72 \div 8 =$ _____   p $63 \div 9 =$ _____

q $72 \div 9 =$ _____   r $63 \div 7 =$ _____   s $48 \div 6 =$ _____   t $81 \div 9 =$ _____

u $56 \div 8 =$ _____   v $54 \div 6 =$ _____   w $70 \div 10 =$ _____   x $100 \div 10 =$ _____

Did you know?

Some of these facts can be tricky, but remember they are the opposite of multiplication facts. So, if you need to know **63 ÷ 9**, you can think about how many **9**s in **63**. $7 \times 9 = 63$ and $63 \div 9 = 7$

Facts for the 11 and 12 times tables

Explanation

You also need to learn the multiplication and division facts related to the **11** and **12** times tables. Look for patterns in the numbers to help you remember them.

× 11	× 12	÷ 11	÷ 12
$1 \times 11 = 11$	$1 \times 12 = 12$	$11 \div 11 = 1$	$12 \div 12 = 1$
$2 \times 11 = 22$	$2 \times 12 = 24$	$22 \div 11 = 2$	$24 \div 12 = 2$
$3 \times 11 = 33$	$3 \times 12 = 36$	$33 \div 11 = 3$	$36 \div 12 = 3$
$4 \times 11 = 44$	$4 \times 12 = 48$	$44 \div 11 = 4$	$48 \div 12 = 4$
$5 \times 11 = 55$	$5 \times 12 = 60$	$55 \div 11 = 5$	$60 \div 12 = 5$
$6 \times 11 = 66$	$6 \times 12 = 72$	$66 \div 11 = 6$	$72 \div 12 = 6$
$7 \times 11 = 77$	$7 \times 12 = 84$	$77 \div 11 = 7$	$84 \div 12 = 7$
$8 \times 11 = 88$	$8 \times 12 = 96$	$88 \div 11 = 8$	$96 \div 12 = 8$
$9 \times 11 = 99$	$9 \times 12 = 108$	$99 \div 11 = 9$	$108 \div 12 = 9$
$10 \times 11 = 110$	$10 \times 12 = 120$	$110 \div 11 = 10$	$120 \div 12 = 10$
$11 \times 11 = 121$	$11 \times 12 = 132$	$121 \div 11 = 11$	$132 \div 12 = 11$
$12 \times 11 = 132$	$12 \times 12 = 144$	$132 \div 11 = 12$	$144 \div 12 = 12$

Activities

1 Cover the facts above and test yourself on these questions.

a $3 \times 11 =$ _____ b $5 \times 12 =$ _____ c $5 \times 11 =$ _____ d $3 \times 12 =$ _____

e $66 \div 11 =$ _____ f $48 \div 12 =$ _____ g $22 \div 11 =$ _____ h $72 \div 12 =$ _____

i $132 \div 11 =$ _____ j $7 \times 12 =$ _____ k $11 \times 11 =$ _____ l $11 \div 11 =$ _____

m $9 \times 11 =$ _____ n $9 \times 12 =$ _____ o $36 \div 12 =$ _____ p $144 \div 12 =$ _____

2 Try these questions related to all the times tables.

a $6 \times 9 =$ _____ b $8 \times 12 =$ _____ c $8 \times 8 =$ _____ d $5 \times 11 =$ _____

e $108 \div 12 =$ _____ f $56 \div 7 =$ _____ g $88 \div 11 =$ _____ h $9 \div 9 =$ _____

i $132 \div 12 =$ _____ j $7 \times 9 =$ _____ k $12 \times 7 =$ _____ l $24 \div 8 =$ _____

m $7 \times 7 =$ _____ n $9 \times 10 =$ _____ o $45 \div 5 =$ _____ p $121 \div 11 =$ _____

Multiplication & Division

Missing number questions

When finding missing numbers, think about which number in the fact will be the largest. This can help you decide whether to use multiplication or division to find the missing number.

$3 \times \boxed{} = 39$

In this multiplication, the answer (**39**) will be the largest number, so the missing number must be smaller. You can use the **inverse** operation (division) here to find it.

$39 \div 3 = 13$

The missing number is **13**.

$72 \div \boxed{} = 6$

In this division, the first number (**72**) will be the largest number, so the missing number must be smaller. You use division here to find it.

$72 \div 6 = 12$

The missing number is **12**.

$\boxed{} \div 4 = 8$

In this division, the first number (the missing one) will be the largest number. You need to use the inverse operation (multiplication) here to find it.

$4 \times 8 = 32$

The missing number is **32**.

Activities

1 Find each missing number.

a $12 \div \boxed{} = 4$

b $11 \times \boxed{} = 66$

c $\boxed{} \times 9 = 108$

d $\boxed{} \div 3 = 9$

e $36 \div \boxed{} = 4$

f $7 \times \boxed{} = 42$

g $\boxed{} \times 12 = 60$

h $\boxed{} \div 12 = 3$

i $\boxed{} \times 6 = 36$

j $\boxed{} \div 4 = 8$

Multiplying by one and zero and dividing by one

Explanation

When a number is multiplied by **1** it remains the same, **5 × 1 = 5**.

Similarly, dividing a number by **1** leaves it unchanged, **12 ÷ 1 = 12**.

When any number is multiplied by zero the answer is always zero. **6 × 0** or **0 × 6** will give the answer zero. Imagine 'no lots of six' or 'six lots of nothing' – the answer will be zero.

Activities

1 Answer these questions.

a 3 × 1 = _____   b 5 × 0 = _____   c 3 ÷ 1 = _____   d 0 × 12 = _____

e 8 × 0 = _____   f 1 × 10 = _____   g 1 ÷ 1 = _____   h 0 × 1 = _____

i 1 × 1 = _____   j 7 × 0 = _____   k 8 ÷ 1 = _____   l 11 × 0 = _____

2 Find each missing number.

a 12 ÷ ☐ = 12   b 1 × ☐ = 11

c ☐ × 9 = 9   d ☐ ÷ 3 = 3

e ☐ × 3 = 0   f ☐ ÷ 1 = 3

g 11 ÷ ☐ = 11   h 8 × ☐ = 0

i ☐ × 12 = 12   j ☐ ÷ 1 = 0

3 Are these statements true or false?

a A number multiplied by zero gives the number. _____

b One divided by a number gives the number. _____

c A number divided by one gives the number. _____

Doubling and halving 2

Explanation

Doubling can help you to multiply numbers. To multiply a number:

by **2** – double it $19 \times 2 = 38$

by **4** – double and double again $19 \times 2 = 38$, $38 \times 2 = 76$

by **8** – double, double and double again $19 \times 2 = 38$, $38 \times 2 = 76$, $76 \times 2 = 152$

Halving can help you to divide numbers. To divide a number:

by **2** – halve it $128 \div 2 = 64$

by **4** – halve and halve again $128 \div 2 = 64$, $64 \div 2 = 32$

by **8** – halve, halve and halve again $128 \div 2 = 64$, $64 \div 2 = 32$, $32 \div 2 = 16$

Activities

1 Answer these questions, using doubling and halving.

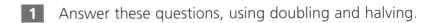

a $7 \times 4 = $ _____   b $7 \times 8 = $ _____   c $9 \times 4 = $ _____   d $25 \times 8 = $ _____

e $48 \div 4 = $ _____   f $48 \div 8 = $ _____   g $52 \div 4 = $ _____   h $64 \div 8 = $ _____

If you want to multiply **5** by an even number, you can double the **5** and halve the even number.

This makes it easier because you can then multiply by **10**.

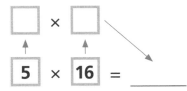

$5 \times 36 = 180$

(double)   (half)

$10 \times 18 = 180$

---

2 To answer these questions, **double** the first number and **halve** the other.

a $\boxed{10} \times \boxed{9}$

$\boxed{5} \times \boxed{18} = \underline{\ 90\ }$

b $\boxed{} \times \boxed{}$

$\boxed{5} \times \boxed{14} = $ _____

c $\boxed{} \times \boxed{}$

$\boxed{5} \times \boxed{16} = $ _____

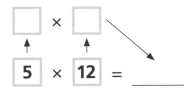

d $\boxed{} \times \boxed{}$

$\boxed{5} \times \boxed{12} = $ _____

e $\boxed{} \times \boxed{}$

$\boxed{5} \times \boxed{24} = $ _____

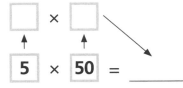

f $\boxed{} \times \boxed{}$

$\boxed{5} \times \boxed{50} = $ _____

Recognising multiples

Explanation

It is important to be able to recognise multiples of the numbers to **12**.

Here are some patterns that make it easier to recognise multiples:

- multiples of **10** end in **0**
- multiples of **5** end in **0** and **5**
- multiples of **2** are even
- multiples of **4** are even and when they are halved the answer is even
- multiples of **8** are even and are also even when halved – when halved again the answer is still even
- multiples of **9** have digits that add to make a multiple of **9**, for example **63 → 6 + 3 = 9**.

Activities

1   Draw a ring around the numbers that match the heading in each box.

a

Multiples of **4**

15	44	7
41	9	12
6	60	27

b

Multiples of **8**

48	32	36
42	56	12
54	96	27

c

Multiples of **9**

36	44	72
46	99	81
63	88	27

d

Multiples of **5**

25	37	9
42	18	12
15	40	27

2   Use the key to draw the correct shapes around the numbers.

50   100   36   40   30

160

12   32   56   84   120

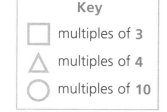

Key

☐	multiples of **3**
△	multiples of **4**
○	multiples of **10**

Multiplying by 10 and 100

Explanation

Multiplying by 10

When multiplying by **10**, move each digit of the other number **one** place to the **left**.
Use zeros to show the empty columns.

Example **637 × 10 = 6370**

Multiplying by 100

When multiplying by **100**, move each digit **two** places to the **left**.
Use zeros to show the empty columns.

Example **637 × 100 = 63 700**

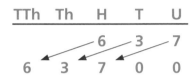

Activities

1 Multiply these numbers by **10**.

a 9 → ___90___	**b** 25 → _____	**c** 43 → _____
d 80 → _____	**e** 378 → _____	**f** 593 → _____
g 682 → _____	**h** 8036 → _____	**i** 6820 → _____

2 Change these prices from pounds to pence by multiplying by **100**.

a £2 → ___200p___	**b** £9 → _____	**c** £17 → _____
d £69 → _____	**e** £127 → _____	**f** £659 → _____
g £806 → _____	**h** £2743 → _____	**i** £5280 → _____

3 Change these lengths from metres to centimetres by multiplying by **100**.

a 5m → ___500cm___	**b** 8m → _____	**c** 23m → _____
d 75m → _____	**e** 341m → _____	**f** 555m → _____
g 904m → _____	**h** 3680m → _____	**i** 6900m → _____

Multiplying three or more numbers together

Activities

1 Answer these questions.

a $4 \times 3 \times 5 =$ _____

b $6 \times 8 \times 5 =$ _____

c $7 \times 3 \times 2 =$ _____

d $4 \times 8 \times 5 =$ _____

e $2 \times 8 \times 4 =$ _____

f $9 \times 5 \times 8 =$ _____

g $3 \times 3 \times 7 =$ _____

h $4 \times 9 \times 2 =$ _____

i $6 \times 7 \times 5 =$ _____

j $2 \times 4 \times 7 =$ _____

2 Answer these questions.

a $4 \times 3 \times 5 \times 3 =$ _____

b $2 \times 8 \times 5 \times 1 =$ _____

c $4 \times 3 \times 5 \times 2 =$ _____

d $5 \times 2 \times 8 \times 5 =$ _____

e $5 \times 3 \times 3 \times 5 =$ _____

f $6 \times 8 \times 5 \times 0 \times 3 \times 5 =$ _____

g $1 \times 1 \times 5 \times 1 \times 1 =$ _____

h $3 \times 1 \times 8 \times 5 =$ _____

Dividing by 10 and 100

Dividing by 10

When dividing by **10**, move each digit of the other number **one** place to the **right**.

Example 57 300 ÷ 10 = 5730

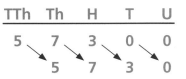

Dividing by 100

When dividing by **100**, move each digit **two** places to the **right**.

Example 57 300 ÷ 100 = 573

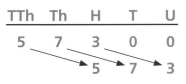

Activities

1 Divide these numbers by **10**.

a 50 → 5   b 70 → _____   c 90 → _____

d 100 → _____   e 280 → _____   f 670 → _____

g 940 → _____   h 4830 → _____   i 5000 → _____

2 Change these prices from pence to pounds by dividing by **100**.

a 300p → £3   b 500p → _____   c 800p → _____

d 900p → _____ e 1400p → _____   f 2400p → _____

g 36 200p → _____ h 56 700p → _____   i 40 000p → _____

3 Change these lengths from centimetres to metres by dividing by **100**.

a 600cm → 6m   b 900cm → _____   c 3400cm → _____

d 5300cm → _____ e 36 700cm → _____   f 68 300cm → _____

g 90 200cm → _____ h 56 200cm → _____   i 73 000cm → _____

Progress test 2

1   Use doubling and halving to answer these questions.

    a $13 \times 4 =$ _____   **b** $8 \times 8 =$ _____   **c** $13 \times 8 =$ _____

    d $72 \div 4 =$ _____   **e** $108 \div 4 =$ _____   **f** $56 \div 8 =$ _____

2   Multiply these numbers by **10**.

    a   28   → _____   **b**   537 → _____   **c**   2043 → _____

    d   308 → _____   **e**   462 → _____   **f**   1204 → _____

3   Multiply these numbers by **100**.

    a   16   → _____   **b**   386 → _____   **c**   4037 → _____

    d   80   → _____   **e**   406 → _____   **f**   3200 → _____

4   Divide these numbers by **10**.

    a   70   → _____   **b**   90   → _____   **c**   300   → _____

    d   640 → _____   **e**   2380 → _____   **f**   5100 → _____

5   Divide these numbers by **100**.

    a   600   → _____   **b**   800   → _____   **c**   1300   → _____

    d   7000 → _____   **e**   31 800 → _____   **f**   89 000 → _____

6   Answer these questions.

    a $9 \times 9 =$ _____   **b** $6 \times 7 =$ _____   **c** $9 \times 6 =$ _____

    d $8 \times 3 =$ _____   **e** $6 \times 8 =$ _____   **f** $8 \times 9 =$ _____

7   Answer these questions.

    a $36 \div 6 =$ _____   **b** $45 \div 9 =$ _____   **c** $49 \div 7 =$ _____

    d $56 \div 7 =$ _____   **e** $72 \div 8 =$ _____   **f** $63 \div 9 =$ _____

  Multiplication & Division

Multiplying 2-digit numbers by single digits

Explanation

Here you need to know how to multiply numbers like **20**, **30**, **40** and **50** by a single number.

$$\boxed{50 \times 6} = 5 \times 6 \times 10$$
$$= 30 \times 10 = 300$$

$$\boxed{70 \times 5} = 7 \times 5 \times 10$$
$$= 35 \times 10 = 350$$

Activities

1 Write the answers.

a $40 \times 2 = $ _____

b $30 \times 4 = $ _____

c $50 \times 8 = $ _____

d $70 \times 6 = $ _____

e $90 \times 6 = $ _____

f $80 \times 8 = $ _____

g $20 \times 3 = $ _____

h $60 \times 2 = $ _____

i $30 \times 6 = $ _____

Partitioning into tens and units

Partitioning can be used to make calculations more manageable.

Example 46 × 7 Approximate first to check your answer.

- Write the question.

- Split **46** into **40** and **6**.

- Multiply each of these by **7**.

$$46 \times 7 =$$ *(Approx. **50 × 7 = 350**)*

$$\underline{40 \times 7} + \underline{6 \times 7}$$

$$280 \quad + \quad 42 = 322$$

---

2 Use partitioning to multiply these numbers.

a $25 \times 5 = $ _____

b $34 \times 4 = $ _____

c $39 \times 5 = $ _____

d $42 \times 6 = $ _____

e $43 \times 7 = $ _____

f $52 \times 5 = $ _____

g $64 \times 6 = $ _____

h $71 \times 7 = $ _____

i $82 \times 8 = $ _____

Column multiplication

Explanation

On pages 12 and 25 you learnt how to partition to multiply 2-digit numbers.
You can set the questions out in columns to make the multiplication easier, like this.

Example 62 × 7   *(Approx. 60 × 7 = 420)*

	H	T	U
		6	2
×			7
2 × 7 →		1	4
60 × 7 →	4	2	0 →
	4	3	4

Because the answer to **60 × 7** will be **10** times larger than **6 × 7**, put a **0** to make the answer **10** times larger.

Check the answer against your approximation.

Activities

1   Use this column method to multiply these numbers.

a   4 6
    ×   5

b   5 7
    ×   3

c   8 3
    ×   4

d   3 9
    ×   8

e   5 8
    ×   6

f   9 6
    ×   4

g   7 7
    ×   5

h   6 4
    ×   9

i   8 6
    ×   7

Short multiplication 1

Explanation

When you feel confident using column multiplication, you can use short multiplication, which is quicker. Follow the boxes if you're not sure.

Example 62 × 7   *(Approx. **60 × 7 = 420**)*

```
    H    T    U
         6    2
    ×         7
   ─────────────
    4    3    4        Check the answer against your approximation.
              1
```

←──────────────────────────────── start here

(**7 × 6** tens) + **1** ten = **43** tens. Write **43**. ←── **7 × 2 = 14**, write **4** and carry **1** ten into the tens column.

Activities

1 Use short multiplication to answer these questions.

a 4 3 × 5	**b** 2 7 × 5	**c** 4 3 × 4
d 4 7 × 3	**e** 5 7 × 4	**f** 8 3 × 8
g 3 3 × 6	**h** 6 4 × 5	**i** 8 7 × 6
j 6 9 × 5	**k** 8 7 × 9	**l** 7 7 × 7

Multiplying 3-digit numbers by single digits

Explanation

Here you need to know how to multiply numbers like **200**, **300** and **400** by a single number.

$$500 \times 6 \quad = 5 \times 6 \times 100$$
$$= 30 \times 100 = 3000$$

$$700 \times 5 \quad = 7 \times 5 \times 100$$
$$= 35 \times 10 = 3500$$

Activities

1 Write the answers.

a $400 \times 2 =$ _____

b $300 \times 4 =$ _____

c $500 \times 8 =$ _____

d $700 \times 6 =$ _____

e $900 \times 6 =$ _____

f $800 \times 8 =$ _____

Partitioning into hundreds, tens and units

You can also partition numbers into hundreds, tens and units.

Example 237×6

- Write the question.

$$237 \times 6 = \qquad \text{(Approx. } 250 \times 6 = 1500\text{)}$$

- Split **237** into **200**, **30** and **7**.

$$\underline{200 \times 6} + \underline{30 \times 6} + \underline{7 \times 6}$$

- Multiply each of these by **6**.

$$1200 \ + \ 180 \ + \ 42 \ = 1422$$

2 Use partitioning to multiply these numbers.

a $124 \times 4 =$ _____

b $164 \times 5 =$ _____

c $249 \times 5 =$ _____

d $342 \times 6 =$ _____

e $473 \times 6 =$ _____

f $518 \times 6 =$ _____

g $564 \times 7 =$ _____

h $641 \times 8 =$ _____

i $782 \times 9 =$ _____

Simple division and finding remainders

If **12** biscuits are shared between **3** people they each get **4**. There are no biscuits left over because **4** divides exactly into **12**.

$$12 \div 3 = 4$$

If **14** biscuits are shared between **3** people they each get **4** but there are **2** biscuits left over.

$$14 \div 3 = 4$$
with **2** left over

14 divided by **3** is **4** remainder **2**.

$$14 \div 3 = 4 \ r2$$

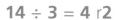

Activities

1   Answer these questions.

a $13 \div 3 =$ __4 r1__   b $11 \div 3 =$ _____   c $14 \div 3 =$ _____

d $17 \div 3 =$ _____   e $19 \div 3 =$ _____   f $25 \div 3 =$ _____

Multiples of a number can be shown on a counting stick.
Count up in fours from zero to show the multiples of **4**. They are shown beneath this line.

0	1	2	3	4	5	6	7	8	9	10
0	4	8	12	16	20	24	28	32	36	40

Can you see how to find the answer to these? $20 \div 4 = 5$ $24 \div 4 = 6$

If the number to be divided is not a multiple of **4** you can give your answer with a remainder, like this. $25 \div 4 = 6 \ r1$

Look for the multiple of **4** just less than the number. **24** is **1** less than **25** so there is a remainder of **1**.

---

2   Answer these questions.

a $19 \div 4 =$ _____   b $22 \div 4 =$ _____   c $27 \div 4 =$ _____

d $29 \div 4 =$ _____   e $33 \div 4 =$ _____   f $35 \div 4 =$ _____

3   Use the multiples of **5** to answer these.

a $19 \div 5 =$ _____   b $24 \div 5 =$ _____   c $29 \div 5 =$ _____

d $37 \div 5 =$ _____   e $43 \div 5 =$ _____   f $46 \div 5 =$ _____

Setting out division questions

Divisions can be set out in different ways.
One way is using the ÷ division sign, for example: $27 \div 3 = 9$

Divisions can also be shown using fraction notation, like this: $\frac{1}{3}$ of **27** = **9**

Another way of setting divisions out is using the $\overline{)\quad}$ sign.

$3\overline{)27}$ means **27** divided by **3**. When we use this notation we write the answer on the top of the line, like this: $3\overline{)27}^{\,9}$

Activities

1 Answer these division questions.

a $35 \div 5 =$ _____

b $\frac{1}{3}$ of **30** = _____

c $32 \div 4 =$ _____

d $\frac{1}{8}$ of **80** = _____

e $40 \div 8 =$ _____

f $\frac{1}{9}$ of **63** = _____

g $99 \div 11 =$ _____

h $\frac{1}{6}$ of **36** = _____

i $84 \div 12 =$ _____

j $\frac{1}{7}$ of **56** = _____

2 Answer these division questions, writing the answers above the lines.

a $4\overline{)32}$

b $8\overline{)64}$

c $6\overline{)30}$

d $3\overline{)36}$

e $6\overline{)72}$

f $7\overline{)77}$

Factors

Explanation

Factors are whole numbers that divide exactly into another number.

Example To find the factors of **18**:

- look for pairs of numbers that multiply to make **18**

1×18 2×9 3×6

- write the numbers in order **1**, **2**, **3**, **6**, **9**, **18** – these are the factors of **18**.

Activities

1   Write the factors of the number in the flower on the petals.

a

b

c

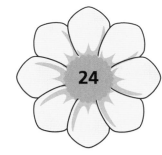

d

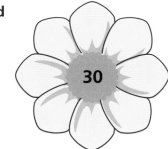

e

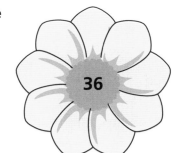

f

Using factors can make it easier to multiply in your head.

Example 25×18 **6** and **3** are factors of **18**, so you can break **18** into 6×3 and the question becomes:

$25 \times 6 \times 3$ $25 \times 6 = 150$ and $150 \times 3 = 450$, so $25 \times 18 = 450$

---

2   Use factors to help you answer these questions.

a $25 \times 8 =$ _____

b $15 \times 6 =$ _____

c $25 \times 12 =$ _____

d $30 \times 14 =$ _____

e $30 \times 16 =$ _____

f $40 \times 12 =$ _____

g $40 \times 15 =$ _____

h $35 \times 12 =$ _____

i $45 \times 16 =$ _____

Square numbers

Explanation

Square numbers are called square because they can be drawn as squares.

| 1 | 4 | 9 | 16 | 25 | 36 | 49 |

Square numbers are the result of multiplying a number by itself.

Example $1 \times 1 = 1$ $2 \times 2 = 4$ $8 \times 8 = 64$ $10 \times 10 = 100$ $200 \times 200 = 40\,000$

Activities

1 Write the answers to the following questions.

a $2 \times 2 = 2$ squared   = _____

b $5 \times 5 = 5$ squared = _____

c $10 \times 10 = 10$ squared = _____

d $4 \times 4 = 4$ squared = _____

e $8 \times 8 = 8$ squared   = _____

f $7 \times 7 = 7$ squared = _____

Use a small raised ² to mean squared.

Example 3^2 means **3** squared or 3×3, which equals **9**.
$$5^2 = 5 \times 5 = 25 \qquad 10^2 = 10 \times 10 = 100$$

---

2 Join any tickets that show the same amount.

| 9^2 | 4^2 | 81 | 12×12 | 8×8 | 64 |

| 11^2 | 7×7 | 7^2 | 9×9 | 16 |

| 11×11 | 36 | 4×4 | 6×6 | 49 |

| 12^2 | 8^2 | 6^2 | 121 | 144 |

Cube numbers

Explanation

Some numbers are known as cube numbers, such as **1**, **8**, **27** and **64**. Cube numbers are called this as they can be made from this number of small cubes.

 1   8   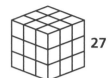 27   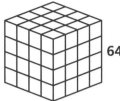 64

Cube numbers are the result of multiplying three of the same number together, like this.

Example $1 \times 1 \times 1 = 1$, $2 \times 2 \times 2 = 8$, $3 \times 3 \times 3 = 27$, $4 \times 4 \times 4 = 64$, $5 \times 5 \times 5 = 125$...

Use a small raised ^{3} to mean cubed.

Example 3^3 means **3 cubed** or **3 × 3 × 3**, which equals **27**.

Activities

1 Join any tickets that show the same amount.

10^3	4^3	216	3^3	6 × 6 × 6	2^3
1^3	1000	1 × 1 × 1	3 × 3 × 3	1
10 × 10 × 10	5 × 5 × 5	2 × 2 × 2	4 × 4 × 4	64
27	8	5^3	6^3	125

2 Write the answers to the following questions.

a $1^3 =$ _____1_____   b _____ $^3 = 27$

c _____ $^3 = 216$ d $10^3 =$ _____

e $20^3 =$ _____   f $30^3 =$ _____

3 Calculate the following using appropriate multiplication methods.

a $7^3 = 7 \times 7 \times 7 = 49 \times 7 =$ _____

b $9^3 = 9 \times 9 \times 9 = 81 \times 9 =$ _____

Distributive law

Explanation

When multiplying a number, you can split it into parts, multiply each part separately and then add the answers together.

These diagrams show different ways that **13** can be split to help find the answer to **6 × 13**.

13 split into **4** and **9**

6 × 4   **6 × 9**

X X X X | X X X X X X X X X
X X X X | X X X X X X X X X
X X X X | X X X X X X X X X
X X X X | X X X X X X X X X
X X X X | X X X X X X X X X
X X X X | X X X X X X X X X

24   **54**

24 + 54 = 78

13 split into **8** and **5**

6 × 8   **6 × 5**

X X X X X X X X | X X X X X
X X X X X X X X | X X X X X
X X X X X X X X | X X X X X
X X X X X X X X | X X X X X
X X X X X X X X | X X X X X
X X X X X X X X | X X X X X

48   **30**

48 + 30 = 78

13 split into **10** and **3**

6 × 10   **6 × 3**

X X X X X X X X X X | X X X
X X X X X X X X X X | X X X
X X X X X X X X X X | X X X
X X X X X X X X X X | X X X
X X X X X X X X X X | X X X
X X X X X X X X X X | X X X

60   **18**

60 + 18 = 78

Activities

1   Answer these.

   a Find the answer to **13 × 8** by splitting **13** into **5** and **8**.

   5 × 8 = _____ and **8 × 8 =** _____ so **13 × 8 =** _____

   b Find the answer to **14 × 7** by splitting **14** into **9** and **5**.

   9 × 7 = _____ and **5 × 7 =** _____ so **14 × 7 =** _____

   c Find the answer to **34 × 6** by splitting **34** into **30** and **4**.

   30 × 6 = _____ and **4 × 6 =** _____ so **34 × 6 =** _____

2   Find the area of each of these rectangles, splitting the larger number to make the multiplication easier.

a

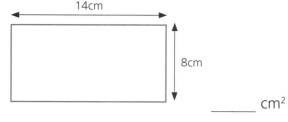

14cm

8cm

_____ cm²

b

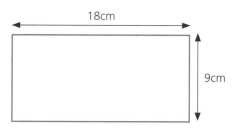

18cm

9cm

_____ cm²

Column and short multiplication

Explanation

On pages 25 and 28 you learnt how to partition to multiply 2- and 3-digit numbers. You can set the questions out in columns to make the multiplication easier.

Check the answer against your approximation.

623 × 7   (Approx. **600 × 7 = 4200**)

	Th	H	T	U
		6	2	3
×				7
7 × 3 →			2	1
7 × 20 →		1	4	0
7 × 600 →	4	2	0	0
	4	3	6	1

Activities

1 Use this method to answer these.

a
```
    4 6 3
×       5
_____
```

b
```
    5 2 7
×       4
_____
```

c
```
    4 8 6
×       6
_____
```

When you feel confident using column multiplication, you can use short multiplication, which is quicker.

Check the answer against your approximation.

623 × 7   (Approx. **600 × 7 = 4200**)

	Th	H	T	U
		6	2	3
×				7
	4	3	6	1
			1	2

(**7 × 6** hundreds) + **1** hundred = **43** hundreds. Write **43**. ← (**7 × 2** tens) + **2** tens = **16** tens. Write **6** and carry **1** hundred into the hundreds column. ← **7 × 3 = 21**. Write **1** in the units column and carry **2** tens into the tens column.

2 Use short multiplication to answer these.

a
```
    7 4 7
×       3
_____
```

b
```
    5 8 7
×       4
_____
```

c
```
    3 9 7
×       6
_____
```

Short multiplication 2

Explanation

On page 27, short multiplication for 2-digit numbers was introduced. This method can be used to multiply larger numbers in the same way. The example below shows short multiplication for multiplying a 4-digit number by a single-digit number.

Example 6234×7

(Approx. 6000 × 7 = 42 000)

	Th	H	T	U
	6	2	3	4
×				7
	4	3	6	3	8
		1	2	2

Check the answer against your approximation.

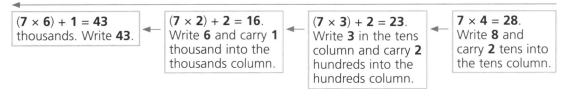

| (7 × 6) + 1 = **43** thousands. Write **43**. | (7 × 2) + 2 = **16**. Write **6** and carry **1** thousand into the thousands column. | (7 × 3) + 2 = **23**. Write **3** in the tens column and carry **2** hundreds into the hundreds column. | 7 × 4 = **28**. Write **8** and carry **2** tens into the tens column. |

Activities

1 Use short multiplication to answer these.

a
```
    8 4 5 7
  ×       3
  _____
```

b
```
    3 6 8 7
  ×       4
  _____
```

c
```
    3 9 7 7
  ×       8
  _____
```

2 Set these out for yourself, then answer the questions.

a $5 \times 4623 =$

b $3 \times 5272 =$

c $4186 \times 4 =$

d $1236 \times 6 =$

e $6179 \times 7 =$

f $8 \times 7372 =$

Multiplication & Division

Written division

It is important to be able to divide on paper. Here is one way, using basic number facts.

Example 692 ÷ 4   (*Approx. **700 ÷ 4 = 175***)

$$100 + 50 + 20 + 3 = 173$$

```
           100 + 50 + 20 + 3 = 173
        4 ) 692
4 × 100   −400   →  There are 4 lots of 100 in 692, leaving 292
           292
4 × 50    −200   →  There are 4 lots of 50 in 292, leaving 92
            92
4 × 20     −80   →  There are 4 lots of 20 in 92, leaving 12
            12
4 × 3      −12   →  There are 4 lots of 3 in 12, leaving 0
             0
```

Activities

1 Try these questions using the method above.

a 5) 1 3 5   b 6) 1 3 8   c 7) 1 4 7

d 6) 3 7 8   e 5) 2 3 5   f 8) 4 5 6

Here are some shorter ways of dividing.

```
           150 + 23 = 173
        4 ) 692
4 × 150  −600
           92
4 × 23    −92
            0
```

This is a shorter version of the method above. Starting with **4 × 150** rather than **4 × 100**. You can use whatever facts you know.

```
          1 7 3
       4 ) 6 ²9 ¹2
```

This is often called short division. **4** into **6** = **1** r**2**. Write **1** above. Carry **2** to make **29**. **4** into **29** = **7** r**1**. Write **7** above. Carry **1** to make **12**. **4** into **12** = **3**. Write **3** above.

---

2 Try these questions using one of the methods above.

a 5) 1 8 5   b 6) 1 8 6   c 7) 1 6 8

d 438 ÷ 6 = _____   e 656 ÷ 8 = _____   f 783 ÷ 9 = _____

Short division 1

Explanation

On page 37, you saw an example of short division. When dividing a 3- or 4-digit number by a single digit, work from the left-hand digit first, dividing each digit and carrying across to the digit to its right where necessary.

Example

$$3 \overline{)7 \ ^14 \ ^22 \ ^15} \quad = 2475$$

Work from left to right.

3 into **7** goes twice. Write **2** above. Carry **1** to make **14**.

3 into **14** goes **4** times. Write **4** above and carry **2** to make **22**.

3 into **22** goes **7** times. Write **7** above and carry **1** to make **15**.

3 into **15** goes **5** times.

Activities

1 Answer these questions using short division.

a $3 \overline{)9642}$

b $4 \overline{)8524}$

c $5 \overline{)6075}$

d $3 \overline{)7497}$

e $4 \overline{)4532}$

f $8 \overline{)9936}$

g $6 \overline{)8604}$

h $3 \overline{)9261}$

Using rounding and inverses to check

Explanation

So far, the example calculations in this book have included approximations or rounding to see whether an answer is 'about right'.

Example 3888 ÷ 8 = 486   *(Approx. **4000 ÷ 8 = 500**)*

Another way of checking is to use inverse operations.

- To check a multiplication, **divide** the answer by a number in the question.
- To check a division, **multiply** the answer by the second number in the question.

If the answer to this calculation is the same as the other number in each question, it is correct.

3888 ÷ 8 = 486   To check this you can **multiply** the answer by one number from the question to give the other number.

```
        4   8   6
    ×           8
    ─────────────
    3   8   8   8       This is correct.
        6   4
```

Activities

1   First write an approximation for each of these multiplications or divisions.

a 196 × 6 = _____

_____ × _____ = _____

b 792 ÷ 4 = _____

_____ ÷ _____ = _____

c 575 ÷ 5 = _____

_____ ÷ _____ = _____

d 186 × 8 = _____

_____ × _____ = _____

e 2028 × 3 = _____

_____ × _____ = _____

f 9592 ÷ 4 = _____

_____ ÷ _____ = _____

2   Now do each of the calculations in activity **1**.

3   Check each answer by doing an inverse calculation. Write the calculations here.

a _____

b _____

c _____

d _____

e _____

f _____

1 Use short multiplication to answer these.

a
```
    6 4
×     7
_____

_____
```

b
```
    3 7
×     6
_____

_____
```

c
```
    7 8
×     5
_____

_____
```

d
```
    3 7
×     9
_____

_____
```

e
```
    6 6
×     4
_____

_____
```

f
```
    7 6
×     8
_____

_____
```

2 Answer these division questions.

a **84 ÷ 7 =** _____

b $\frac{1}{8}$ of **56 =** _____

c $4 \overline{)\ 5\ 2}$

d $8 \overline{)\ 9\ 6}$

3 Draw a square around any numbers that are square numbers.

34   **38**   **85**   **25**   **6**   **9**   **4**   **36**   **100**   **81**   **55**

4 Draw a ring around any numbers that are cube numbers.

85   **27**   **8**   **9**   **1**   **36**   **100**   **81**   **55**   **1000**

5 Use short multiplication to answer these.

a
```
  8 4 5 7
×       6
_____

_____
```

b
```
  3 6 8 7
×       5
_____

_____
```

c
```
  3 9 7 8
×       7
_____

_____
```

6 Answer these questions using short division.

a $3 \overline{)\ 6\ 3\ 4\ 2}$

b $4 \overline{)\ 9\ 5\ 2\ 8}$

Short division 2

Explanation

When using short division, sometimes there will be remainders.

Example

$$0\ 5\ 7\ 0\ \text{r}5$$
$$6\overline{)3\ ^34\ ^42\ 5}$$

$$3425 \div 6 = 570\,\text{r}5$$

Work from left to right.

6 into **3** doesn't go so write **0** above and carry **3** to make **34**.

6 into **34** goes **5** times. Write **5** above and carry **4** to make **42**.

6 into **42** goes **7** times. Write **7** above.

6 doesn't go into **5**, so write **0** above and write the **5** as a remainder.

Activities

1 Answer these division questions using short division and giving remainders.

a $7\overline{)4\ 5\ 3\ 2}$

b $6\overline{)2\ 9\ 3\ 7}$

c $8\overline{)8\ 6\ 0\ 5}$

d $5\overline{)3\ 2\ 6\ 2}$

e $4\overline{)3\ 6\ 4\ 3}$

f $3\overline{)2\ 5\ 2\ 4}$

2 Which of these questions have a remainder of **1**? _____ and _____

a $5\overline{)4\ 0\ 7\ 6}$

b $3\overline{)2\ 5\ 9\ 8}$

c $6\overline{)4\ 5\ 3\ 1}$

d $7\overline{)2\ 9\ 3\ 7}$

Remainders as fractions

You can give answers to division questions as mixed numbers rather than using remainders. For example, when dividing **45** by **2** the answer could be given as **22** r**1** or **22**$\frac{1}{2}$. To decide what the fraction should be, write any remainder as the numerator (top number) of the fraction and the number you are dividing by as the denominator (bottom number).

Example

$$6 \overline{)\ 3\ ^34\ ^42\ 5} = 0\ 5\ 7\ 0\ \tfrac{5}{6}$$

$$3425 \div 6 = 570\tfrac{5}{6}$$

Activities

1 Rewrite each of these answers giving the remainder as a fraction.

a $5737 \div 4 = 1434$ r1 = _____

b $9362 \div 7 = 1337$ r3 = _____

c $7630 \div 9 = 847$ r7 = _____

d $8624 \div 5 = 1724$ r4 = _____

2 Simplify the fractions for these, if you can.

a $5738 \div 4 = 1434$ r2 = _____

b $6666 \div 8 = 833$ r2 = _____

c $7565 \div 10 = 756$ r5 = _____

3 Answer these divisions using short division, and giving remainders as simplified fractions.

a $8 \overline{)\ 4\ 5\ 3\ 4}$

b $6 \overline{)\ 1\ 9\ 3\ 5}$

c $9 \overline{)\ 4\ 1\ 0\ 7}$

d $4 \overline{)\ 3\ 2\ 6\ 2}$

Rounding remainders up or down

Explanation

When faced with a problem that involves division, it is sometimes necessary to round the answer up or down rather than giving a remainder.

Example **22** children are going on a school trip. Each car can carry **four** children.

How many cars will be needed?

Which of these answers is right?

| 5 r2 | $5\frac{1}{2}$ | 5 | 6 |

The answer is **6** because, although there will only be two children in the sixth car, that car is still needed.

Look out for remainders and think carefully about what they mean in each problem.

In some problems you will need to round up to the next whole number and in others you will need to round down to the previous whole number.

Activities

1 Solve these problems.

a A school has £**54** to buy basketballs. Each ball costs £**4**.
How many balls can they buy? _____

b I have **62** cakes. Each box holds eight cakes.
How many boxes do I need? _____

c **47** eggs are put into boxes that each hold six eggs.
How many boxes are needed? _____

d **47** eggs are put into boxes, that each hold six eggs.
How many boxes will be full? _____

e A florist has **44** roses. She puts them into vases with
five roses in each vase. How many full vases are there? _____

f Each online photo folder shows six photos.
What is the smallest number of folders that I
need to hold **74** photos? _____

g Abigail has £**58** to buy some new DVDs. Each DVD costs £**9**.
How many DVDs can she buy? _____

Scaling

Explanation

Example A shop has a special offer. For every **three** apples you buy, they give you **two** for free. How many free apples will you get if you buy **21** apples?

As the number of apples you buy increases, so does the number you get free. This is known as **scaling**. By writing the multiples of **3** and then the multiples of **2** beneath them you can see a pattern.

Number of apples you buy	3	6	9	12	15	18	21
Number of apples you get free	2	4	6	8	10	12	14

Each pair of numbers shows you how many you would get free for each number of apples you buy. So, if you buy **21** apples, you get **14** apples free.

Activities

1 A sweet shop has a special offer. For every five sweets you buy, they give you two sweets for free. Complete the lines of multiples.

Number of sweets you buy	5	10	____	____	____	____	____
Number of sweets you get free	2	4	____	____	____	____	____

How many free sweets will you get if you buy **35** sweets? _____

2 Tennis balls are sold in packs of four balls. Each pack costs £**9**.
How many balls would you get if you paid £**81**? _____

Cost	£9	£ ____	____	____	____	____	____	____	____
Number of balls	4	8	____	____	____	____	____	____	____

3 Eggs are sold in boxes of six. Each box costs £**2**.
How many eggs would you get if you paid £**16**? _____

4 A new plant grows seven new leaves every three years.
How many leaves will it have grown after **24** years? _____

Grid multiplication

Grid multiplication uses the partitioning you looked at on page 28.

Split the numbers into hundreds, tens and units or even thousands, hundreds, tens and units and multiply them separately. Then add all the answers together.

Example 7×6234 Always get an approximate answer first: $7 \times 6000 = 42\,000$

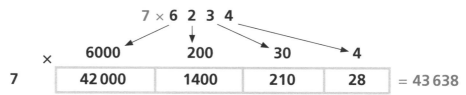

$$7 \times 6\ 2\ 3\ 4$$

$\times$	6000	200	30	4	
7	42 000	1400	210	28	$= 43\,638$

Check the answer against your approximation.

Activities

1 Use grid multiplication to multiply these numbers.

a $4 \times 248 =$ _____

$\times$	200	40	8
4			

b $5 \times 387 =$ _____

$\times$	300	80	7
5			

c $6 \times 472 =$ _____

$\times$			

d $7 \times 539 =$ _____

$\times$			

e $632 \times 8 =$ _____

$\times$			

f $746 \times 9 =$ _____

$\times$			

g $4 \times 2634 =$ _____

$\times$			

h $5 \times 3628 =$ _____

$\times$				

i $6 \times 5729 =$ _____

$\times$			

j $7 \times 6285 =$ _____

$\times$				

Grid and long multiplication

Grid multiplication

Sometimes you have to multiply by 2-digit numbers. You can do it using the grid method.

Example 24×682 Always get an approximate answer first: *20 × 700 = 14 000*

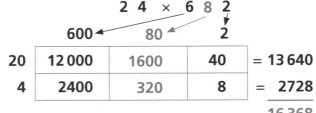

	600	80	2	
20	12 000	1600	40	= 13 640
4	2400	320	8	= 2728

16 368

Check the answer against your approximation.

Activities

1 Use this method to multiply these numbers.

a $17 \times 341 =$ _____   b $32 \times 453 =$ _____   c $45 \times 516 =$ _____

d $362 \times 57 =$ _____   e $473 \times 38 =$ _____   f $603 \times 54 =$ _____

Long multiplication

Here is another way. This method is known as long multiplication.

Example 527×36 *(Approx. 500 × 40 = 20 000)*

```
              5   2   7
        ×         3   6
      ─────────────────
30 × 527 → 1  5   8   1   0
6 × 527  → +  3   1   6   2
      ─────────────────
         1  8   9   7   2
```

Because the answer to **30 × 527** will be **10** times larger than **3 × 527**, put a **0** to make the answer **10** times larger and then multiply **527** by **3**.

Multiply **527** by **6**.

Add the digits of the two answers.

Check the answer against your approximation.

2 Use this method to multiply these numbers.

a $327 \times 24 =$ _____   b $462 \times 43 =$ _____

c $538 \times 56 =$ _____   d $639 \times 58 =$ _____

e $8027 \times 48 =$ _____   f $8735 \times 97 =$ _____

Remainders as decimals

Explanation

Remainders can also be given as decimals. By continuing the short division method you can find decimals. Remember that **1146** is the same as **1146.00** or **1146.000**. You can keep writing zeros after the decimal point without changing the number.

Example

$$8 \overline{)1\ ^11\ ^34\ ^26\ .^20\ ^40}$$
$$0\ 1\ 4\ 3 . 2\ 5$$

$$1146 \div 8 = 143.25$$

Work from left to right.

8 into **1** doesn't go, so write **0** above and carry **1**.

8 into **11** goes once. Write **1** above and carry **3** to make **34**.

8 into **34** goes **4** times. Write **4** above and carry **2** to make **26**.

8 into **26** goes **3** times. Write **3** above and carry **2** to make **20**.

8 into **20** goes **2** times. Write **2** above and carry **4** to make **40**.

8 into **40** goes **5** times. Write **5** above.

Remember to put a decimal point at the end of the number being divided and another above it in the answer.

Activities

1 Answer these division questions using short division and giving remainders as decimals.

a $8 \overline{)\ 4\ 5\ 3\ 2\ .\ 0}$

b $4 \overline{)\ 2\ 9\ 3\ 7}$

c $8 \overline{)\ 8\ 6\ 0\ 6}$

d $5 \overline{)\ 4\ 2\ 6\ 2}$

e $4 \overline{)\ 3\ 2\ 4\ 3}$

f $5 \overline{)\ 7\ 8\ 5\ 7}$

2 Rewrite each of these answers, giving the remainder as a fraction and then as a decimal.

a $537 \div 4 = 134 \text{ r}1 = $ _____ $= $ _____

b $4262 \div 8 = 532 \text{ r}6 = $ _____ $= $ _____

Division word problems

Explanation

On page 43 you saw that some division problems should be answered by rounding any remainder up or down. Some problems, though, are better answered by giving the remainder as a fraction or decimal. It is important to be able to decide how best to answer each question. Look at these three examples.

Four people share **11** cakes equally. How much cake does each person get?

11 ÷ 4 = 2 r3   This is not a sensible answer as the remaining cake is also shared between four people. The answer $2\frac{3}{4}$ cakes is a much more sensible answer.

Four people share £**11** equally. How much does each person get?

11 ÷ 4 = 2 r3   This is not a sensible answer as the remaining pound is also shared between four people. The answer £**2.75** is a much more sensible answer in this instance.

Each car holds up to four people. If there are **11** people, what is the smallest number of cars needed to take them on a journey?

11 ÷ 4 = 2 r3   This is not a sensible answer as the remaining people will also need to go in a car. The answer **three** cars is a better answer.

Activities

1   Answer these questions. Choose whether you think it is best to give each answer with a remainder, with a fraction, as a decimal or by rounding the answer.

a   Four people equally share **5** litres of cola.
     How much do they each drink?   _____

b   Six pizzas are shared equally among five people.
     How much pizza does each person have?   _____

c   A **6**m piece of string is cut into four equal pieces.
     What is the length of each piece?   _____

d   How many **5**p stamps can I buy with **72**p?   _____

e   Four people equally share £**30**. How much do they each get?   _____

f   I need **62** envelopes. How many packs of four must I buy?   _____

Long division 1

Explanation

Long division is a method of division that can help you to divide by 2-digit numbers. The method involves a repeating pattern: **divide**, **multiply**, **subtract**. After each subtraction bring down the next digit.

- To **divide** by **11**, look at the first two digits of the other number together.
  Ask: *'How many 11s in 68?'* There are **6**, so write **6** above the tens digit.

- Point to the **6** you have just written and **multiply** it by **11**. *'6 times 11 = 66'*. Write the answer (**66**) under the **68**. Draw a line under it and **subtract** it. **68 − 66 = 2**

- Bring down the next digit to give **25**.
  Ask: *'How many 11s in 25?'* There are **2**, so write **2** at the top above the units digit.

- Point to the **2** you have just written and **multiply** it by **11**. *'2 times 11 = 22'*. Write the answer (**22**), under the **25**. Draw a line under it and **subtract** it. **25 − 22 = 3**

- As there are no more digits to divide, write the remainder **3** at the top to complete the answer.

			6	2	r3
1	1	6	8	5	
		−	6	6	
			2	5	
		−	2	2	
				3	

Activities

1 Answer these division questions using long division. Give remainders as numbers.

a 11) 4 5 3

b 11) 9 3 7

c 11) 2 4 3

d 11) 7 8 5

Long division 2

Explanation

When doing long division, it can be useful to list the multiples of the number you are dividing by.

- Look at the first two digits of **4554**.
  Ask: *'How many 12s in 45?'*
  There are **3**, so write **3** above.

- **3 × 12 = 36**. Write the answer below
  and **subtract** it. **45 − 36 = 9**

- Bring down the next digit to give **95**.
  Ask: *'How many 12s in 95?'*
  There are **7**, so write **7** at the top.

- **7 × 12 = 84**. Write the answer below
  and **subtract** it. **95 − 84 = 11**

- Bring down the next digit to give **114**.
  Ask: *'How many 12s in 114?'*
  There are **9**, so write **9** at the top.

- **9 × 12 = 108**. Write the answer below
  and **subtract** it. **114 − 108 = 6**

- As there are no more digits to divide, write
  the remainder **6** at the top to complete
  the answer.

1	12
2	24
3	36
4	48
5	60
6	72
7	84
8	96
9	108
10	120

```
            3  7  9  r6
1  2 | 4  5  5  4
    -  3  6
          9  5
       -  8  4
          1  1  4
          1  0  8
                6
```

Activities

1 Answer these division questions using long division. Give remainders as numbers.

a 12) 4 5 3 2

b 12) 2 9 3 7

c 12) 3 2 4 3

d 12) 7 8 5 7

Multiplying and dividing by 10 and 100

On page 21 you learnt

Explanation

Multiplying by 10 and 100

On page 21 you learnt that when multiplying by **10**, move each digit **one** place to the left, and when multiplying by **100** move each digit **two** places to the left. The same applies for decimals, such as those with digits that are tenths and hundredths.

$$5.29 \times 10 = 52.9$$

H	T	U . t	h
		5 . 2	9
5	2 . 9		

$$5.29 \times 100 = 529$$

H	T	U . t	h
		5 . 2	9
5	2	9	

Activities

1 Answer these questions.

a   4.6 × 100 = _____

b   5.43 × 10 = _____

c   2.6 × 10 = _____

d   0.48 × 100 = _____

e   46.7 × 100 = _____

f   12.3 × 100 = _____

Dividing by 10 and 100

On page 23 you learnt that when dividing by **10** move each digit **one** place to the right, and when dividing by **100** move each digit **two** places to the right. The same applies for decimals, such as those with digits that are tenths and hundredths.

$$68.3 \div 10 = 6.83$$

H	T	U . t	h	th
	6	8 . 3		
		6 . 8	3	

$$68.3 \div 100 = 0.683$$

H	T	U . t	h	th
	6	8 . 3		
		. 6	8	3

2 Answer these questions.

a   2 ÷ 10 = _____

b   48 ÷ 10 = _____

c   54 ÷ 100 = _____

d   50 ÷ 100 = _____

e   32.1 ÷ 100 = _____

f   4.9 ÷ 10 = _____

Multiplying decimals

Explanation

You can multiply decimals in the same way that you multiply whole numbers.

Always approximate first because then you don't have to worry about the decimal points. Now multiply as if they were whole numbers.

Example **7.84 × 6**   *(Approx. 8 × 6 = 48)*   **2.34 × 2.6**   *(Approx. 2 × 3 = 6)*

		7	8	4
	×			6
700 × 6 →	4	2	0	0
80 × 6 →		4	8	0
4 × 6 →			2	4
	4	7 . 0	4

		2	3	4
	×		2	6
234 × 20 →	4	6	8	0
234 × 6 →	1	4	0	4
	6 . 0	8	4

The answer must be **47.04** rather than **4.704** or **470.4** because our approximation was **48**.

The answer must be **6.084** rather than **60.84** or **608.4** because our approximation was **6**.

Activities

1 Multiply these decimal numbers.

a $5.6 \times 7 =$ _____

b $7.8 \times 5 =$ _____

c $8.3 \times 6 =$ _____

d $6.45 \times 4 =$ _____

e $6.04 \times 7 =$ _____

f $2.39 \times 8 =$ _____

2 Now try these.

a $3.25 \times 4.8 =$ _____

b $4.86 \times 3.2 =$ _____

c $6.28 \times 5.7 =$ _____

d $7.89 \times 4.9 =$ _____

e $8.93 \times 6.2 =$ _____

f $9.04 \times 7.8 =$ _____

Dividing decimals

Explanation

You can divide decimals in the same way that you divide whole numbers.

Always approximate first because then you don't have to worry about the decimal points. Now divide as if they were whole numbers.

Example $19.5 \div 5$ (*Approx.* **19.5** *is about* **20** *and* **20 ÷ 5 = 4**)

$$
\begin{array}{r}
3\ 9 \rightarrow 3.9 \\
5\overline{)\ 1\ 9\ ^45}
\end{array}
$$

5 into **19** = **3** r**4**. Write **3** above. Carry **4** to make **45**. **5** into **45** = **9**. Write **9** above. Look at the approximation to decide where to put the decimal point.

The answer must be **3.9** rather than **39** or **0.39** because our approximation was **4**.

Activities

1   Divide these numbers and shade in your answers in the grid below.

a $5\overline{)\ 1\ 4.5}$

b $6\overline{)\ 1\ 5.6}$

c $7\overline{)\ 2\ 1.7}$

d $6\overline{)\ 8.7\ 6}$

e $5\overline{)\ 9.8\ 5}$

f $8\overline{)\ 8.6\ 4}$

g $65.1 \div 7 = $ _____

h $5.16 \div 6 = $ _____

i $7.56 \div 9 = $ _____

j $41.88 \div 6 = $ _____

k $10.88 \div 8 = $ _____

l $164.5 \div 7 = $ _____

1.36	2.4	3.87	1.9	4.82	3.6
23.5	4.04	9.27	3.1	1.46	9.3
2.9	0.84	2.6	6.98	8.1	0.86
8.3	7.56	4.9	3.7	8.64	1.97
2.7	0.46	6.2	4.86	3.9	1.08

Progress test 4

1 Answer these division questions using short division and giving remainders.

a $7 \overline{) 6\ 8\ 2\ 2}$

b $6 \overline{) 3\ 6\ 3\ 7}$

2 Use short division and give remainders as simplified fractions.

a $8 \overline{) 6\ 7\ 3\ 4}$

b $6 \overline{) 5\ 9\ 3\ 7}$

3 Answer these multiplication questions using long multiplication.

a
$$\begin{array}{r} 3\ 7\ 5 \\ \times\quad 7\ 5 \\ \hline \end{array}$$

b
$$\begin{array}{r} 1\ 3\ 5 \\ \times\quad 3\ 6 \\ \hline \end{array}$$

c
$$\begin{array}{r} 6\ 7\ 8 \\ \times\quad 6\ 8 \\ \hline \end{array}$$

4 Answer these division questions using short division and giving remainders as decimals.

a $5 \overline{) 8\ 6\ 0\ 6}$

b $8 \overline{) 3\ 2\ 6\ 2}$

5 Answer these decimal questions.

a $3.5 \times 4 =$ _____

b $28.3 \times 9 =$ _____

c $4.3 \times 5.78 =$ _____

d $1.46 \times 2.5 =$ _____

e $144.5 \div 4 =$ _____

f $21.693 \div 3 =$ _____

6 Answer these questions using long division and giving remainders.

a $11 \overline{) 4\ 5\ 3\ 4}$

b $12 \overline{) 1\ 9\ 3\ 5}$

Mixed operations

Activities

1 Answer these problems.

a How much cheaper is it to pay **12** monthly payments of **£252** than paying four payments of **£759**?

_____

b Toby buys four DVDs that cost **£4.85** each and pays with a **£20** note. How much change does he get?

_____

c Paige wins **£4959** on the lottery. She uses **£1845** to buy a new car and then shares the rest out equally among her three children. How much does each child get?

_____

d Lily takes **£60** with her to a theme park. She pays **£17** for entry and **£21** for food, and spends the rest on eight rides. If the rides all cost the same, how much did each ride cost?

_____

e Dalip earned **£274** each week for nine weeks. He pays **£352** of this amount in tax and puts the rest into his bank account. There was **£635** in his bank account before he paid the money in. How much is there in his bank account now?

_____

Order of operations and brackets

Explanation

When a calculation has several operations, it is important to know the order in which you should do them. If there are **no brackets**, always do multiplication and divisions first, followed by additions and subtractions after that.

Example $11 + 14 \div 7 =$ Do the **$14 \div 7$** first and then do the addition second, so the answer is $11 + 2 = 13$.

Activities

1   Answer these.

a $12 + 45 \div 9 =$ _____

b $6 + 7 \times 8 =$ _____

c $5 - 10 \div 2 =$ _____

d $8 + 2 \times 2 =$ _____

e $9 + 9 \div 3 - 2 =$ _____

f $8 + 7 \times 2 - 5 =$ _____

When there are **brackets** in the calculation always do that part first, even if it is an addition or subtraction. Once you have done that, follow the order as before.

Example $10 - (5 + 4) \div 3 =$ Do the part in brackets first and then do the division next and finally the subtraction, so the answer is $10 - 3 = 7$.

---

2   Answer the questions in each pair.

a $45 \div 5 + 4 =$ _____

$45 \div (5 + 4) =$ _____

b $6 + 6 \div 2 =$ _____

$(6 + 6) \div 2 =$ _____

c $15 - 10 \div 5 =$ _____

$(15 - 10) \div 5 =$ _____

d $8 + 4 \times 2 =$ _____

$(8 + 4) \times 2 =$ _____

e $8 + 4 \div 4 - 2 =$ _____

$(8 + 4) \div (4 - 2) =$ _____

f $7 + 3 \times 2 - 1 + 3 =$ _____

$(7 + 3) \times (2 - 1) + 3 =$ _____

Multiplication & Division

Final test

1 Use these facts to help you to answer the questions below.

$$42 \div 7 = 6 \qquad 9 \times 8 = 72 \qquad 54 \div 6 = 9$$

a $72 \div 8 = $ _____

b $9 \times 6 = $ _____

c $6 \times 7 = $ _____

2 Answer these questions.

a $8 \times 7 = $ _____

b $7 \times 9 = $ _____

c $5 \times 8 = $ _____

d $7 \times 7 = $ _____

e $8 \times 6 = $ _____

f $9 \times 5 = $ _____

g $4 \times 7 = $ _____

h $9 \times 3 = $ _____

3 To answer these questions, **double** the first number and **halve** the second.

a

b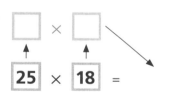

c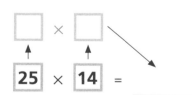

d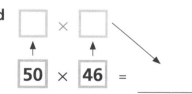

4 Multiply these numbers by **10**.

a $29 \rightarrow$ _____

b $608 \rightarrow$ _____

c $9127 \rightarrow$ _____

5 Multiply these numbers by **100**.

a $24 \rightarrow$ _____

b $536 \rightarrow$ _____

c $8267 \rightarrow$ _____

6 Divide these numbers by **10**.

a 730 → _____   b 1690 → _____   c 3000 → _____

7 Divide these numbers by **100**.

a 6200 → _____   b 7300 → _____   c 86 000 → _____

8 Answer these questions, giving answers with remainders.

a $39 \div 4 =$ _____   b $68 \div 7 =$ _____   c $57 \div 8 =$ _____

9 Write the factors of these numbers.

a 32 → _____

b 72 → _____

10 Use factors to help you answer these questions.

a $25 \times 12 =$ _____   b $45 \times 14 =$ _____

11 Use any method you choose to multiply these numbers.

a $5 \times 572 =$ _____   b $6826 \times 9 =$ _____

12 Use any method you choose to multiply these numbers.

a   7   2   9
    ×   5   8
   _____

b   3   8   0   4
    ×   7   5
   _____

13 Use any method you choose to divide these numbers.

a $6 \overline{) 5\ 6\ 4}$

b $8 \overline{) 7\ 6\ 8}$

14 Multiply these decimal numbers.

a $3.95 \times 8 =$ _____

b $4.37 \times 5.2 =$ _____

15 Divide these decimals.

a $34.8 \div 6 =$ _____

b $6.84 \div 9 =$ _____

16 Solve this problem.

784 sweets are divided equally into **14** bags.
How many sweets are there in five bags?

_____

17 Write the answers to the following questions.

a $1^2 =$ _____

b _____ $^3 = 125$

c _____ $^3 = 27$

d $7 \times 7 \times 7 =$ _____

e **10** squared = _____

f **2** cubed = _____

18 Choose whether you think it is best to give each answer with a remainder, with a fraction, as a decimal or by rounding the answer.

    a Five people equally share £**3**. How much do they each get? _____

    b Seven pizzas are shared equally among five people.
       How much pizza does each person have? _____

19 Use short division and give remainders as simplified fractions.

    a $8\overline{)6366}$ **b** $6\overline{)7833}$

20 Answer these multiplication questions using long multiplication.

    a   7 7 4   **b**   3 3 5   **c**   6 7 3
         ×   4 6   ×   8 6   ×   6 7

21 Answer these.

    a 2.6 × 10 = _____   **b** 0.48 × 100 = _____

22 Answer these division questions using short division and giving remainders as decimals.

    a $5\overline{)4626}$ **b** $8\overline{)2270}$

23 Answer these using long division. Give remainders as fractions.

    a $11\overline{)4525}$ **b** $12\overline{)7569}$

Answers to Activities

Page 4: Multiplying

1.   a 20, 20   b 21, 21   c 18, 18   d 15, 15
   e 40, 40   f 60, 60   g 12, 12   h 10, 10

Page 5: Dividing

1.   a 4   b 5   c 4   d 3
   e 4   f 3   g 2   h 10

Page 6: Links between multiplication and division

1.   a 2   b 12   c 5   d 30

2. The answer is the same as the number you started with. For each multiplication there is a similar division that undoes it.

3.   a 4   b 10   c 20
   d 25   e 4   f 15

Page 7: Learning your 2, 3, 4, 5 and 10 times tables

1.   a 20   b 40   c 21   d 15
   e 90   f 28   g 25   h 12
   i 10   j 33   k 8   l 36
   m 40   n 18   o 120   p 45
   q 18   r 24   s 12   t 16
   u 24   v 24   w 35   x 16

Page 8: Counting in multiples of 2, 3, 4, 5 and 10

1. 5, 10, 15, 20, 25, 30, 35, 40, 45, 50, 55, 60

2. 10, 20, 30, 40, 50, 60, 70, 80, 90, 100, 110, 120

3. Double the multiples of 5 to get the multiples of 10.

4. 2, 4, 6, 8, 10, 12, 14, 16, 18, 20, 22, 24

5. 4, 8, 12, 16, 20, 24, 28, 32, 36, 40, 44, 48

6. Double the multiples of 2 to get the multiples of 4.

7. By doubling the multiples of 4 you get the multiples of 8: 8, 16, 24, 32, 40, 48, 56, 64, 72, 80, 88, 96

Page 9: Division facts 1

1.   a 4   b 11   c 8   d 3
   e 9   f 9   g 8   h 8
   i 6   j 12   k 12   l 11
   m 12   n 8   o 11   p 6
   q 9   r 7   s 12   t 7
   u 9   v 7   w 5   x 7

Page 10: Multiplication and division words

1.   a $3 \times 4 = 12$
   b $9 \div 3 = 3$
   c $7 \times 5 = 35$
   d $18 \div 3 = 6$
   e $4 \times 10 = 40$
   f $120 \div 10 = 12$
   g $66 \div 6 = 11$
   h $24 \div 4 = 6$
   i $50 \div 5 = 10$
   j $4 \times 11 = 44$
   k $12 \times 3 = 36$

2. Answers will vary, e.g. What is 3 times 5?

Page 11: Word problems

1.   a £80   b £8   c 10
   d 11   e 60cm   f 70km
   g 7   h 27   i 9

Page 12: Doubling and halving 1

1.   a 38   b 46   c 72   d 84   e 90
   f 96   g 106   h 136   i 154   j 178

2.   a 31   b 39   c 42   d 46   e 49
   f 52   g 63   h 66   i 84   j 89

Page 14: Learning your 6, 7, 8 and 9 times tables

1
a 30	**b** 56	**c** 49	**d** 18
e 90	**f** 48	**g** 64	**h** 63
i 40	**j** 66	**k** 28	**l** 56
m 81	**n** 42	**o** 108	**p** 36
q 24	**r** 48	**s** 72	**t** 45
u 96	**v** 72	**w** 70	**x** 63

Page 15: Division facts 2

1
a 7	**b** 5	**c** 5	**d** 3
e 4	**f** 6	**g** 6	**h** 8
i 4	**j** 6	**k** 5	**l** 7
m 6	**n** 8	**o** 9	**p** 7
q 8	**r** 9	**s** 8	**t** 9
u 7	**v** 9	**w** 7	**x** 10

Page 16: Facts for the 11 and 12 times tables

1
a 33	**b** 60	**c** 55	**d** 36
e 6	**f** 4	**g** 2	**h** 6
i 12	**j** 84	**k** 121	**l** 1
m 99	**n** 108	**o** 3	**p** 12

2
a 54	**b** 96	**c** 64	**d** 55
e 9	**f** 8	**g** 8	**h** 1
i 11	**j** 63	**k** 84	**l** 3
m 49	**n** 90	**o** 9	**p** 11

Page 17: Missing number questions

1
a 3	**b** 6
c 12	**d** 27
e 9	**f** 6
g 5	**h** 36
i 6	**j** 32

Page 18: Multiplying by one and zero and dividing by one

1
a 3	**b** 0	**c** 3	**d** 0
e 0	**f** 10	**g** 1	**h** 0
i 1	**j** 0	**k** 8	**l** 0

2
a 1	**b** 11
c 1	**d** 9
e 0	**f** 3
g 1	**h** 0
i 1	**j** 0

3
a false
b false
c true

Page 19: Doubling and halving 2

1
a 28	**b** 56	**c** 36	**d** 200
e 12	**f** 6	**g** 13	**h** 8

2
a 90	**b** 70	**c** 80
d 60	**e** 120	**f** 250

Page 20: Recognising multiples

1
a 44, 12, 60
b 48, 32, 56, 96
c 36, 72, 99, 81, 63, 27
d 25, 15, 40

2

Page 21: Multiplying by 10 and 100

1
a 90	**b** 250	**c** 430
d 800	**e** 3780	**f** 5930
g 6820	**h** 80360	**i** 68200

Answers to Activities continued

2 a 200p **b** 900p **c** 1700p
d 6900p **e** 12700p **f** 65900p
g 80600p **h** 274300p **i** 528000p

3 a 500cm **b** 800cm **c** 2300cm
d 7500cm **e** 34100cm **f** 55500cm
g 90400cm **h** 368000cm **i** 690000cm

Page 22: Multiplying three or more numbers together

1 a 60 **b** 240
c 42 **d** 160
e 64 **f** 360
g 63 **h** 72
i 210 **j** 56

2 a 180 **b** 80
c 120 **d** 400
e 225 **f** 0
g 5 **h** 120

Page 23: Dividing by 10 and 100

1 a 5 **b** 7 **c** 9
d 10 **e** 28 **f** 67
g 94 **h** 483 **i** 500

2 a £3 **b** £5 **c** £8
d £9 **e** £14 **f** £24
g £362 **h** £567 **i** £400

3 a 6m **b** 9m **c** 34m
d 53m **e** 367m **f** 683m
g 902m **h** 562m **i** 730m

Page 25: Multiplying 2-digit numbers by single digits

1 a 80 **b** 120 **c** 400
d 420 **e** 540 **f** 640
g 60 **h** 120 **i** 180

2 a 125 **b** 136 **c** 195
d 252 **e** 301 **f** 260
g 384 **h** 497 **i** 656

Page 26: Column multiplication

1 a 230 **b** 171 **c** 332
d 312 **e** 348 **f** 384
g 385 **h** 576 **i** 602

Page 27: Short multiplication 1

1 a 215 **b** 135 **c** 172
d 141 **e** 228 **f** 664
g 198 **h** 320 **i** 522
j 345 **k** 783 **l** 539

Page 28: Multiplying 3-digit numbers by single digits

1 a 800 **b** 1200 **c** 4000
d 4200 **e** 5400 **f** 6400

2 a 496 **b** 820 **c** 1245
d 2052 **e** 2838 **f** 3108
g 3948 **h** 5128 **i** 7038

Page 29: Simple division and finding remainders

1 a 4 r1 **b** 3 r2 **c** 4 r2
d 5 r2 **e** 6 r1 **f** 8 r1

2 a 4 r3 **b** 5 r2 **c** 6 r3
d 7 r1 **e** 8 r1 **f** 8 r3

3 a 3 r4 **b** 4 r4 **c** 5 r4
d 7 r2 **e** 8 r3 **f** 9 r1

Page 30: Setting out division questions

1 a 7 **b** 10
c 8 **d** 10
e 5 **f** 7
g 9 **h** 6
i 7 **j** 8

2 a 8 **b** 8
c 5 **d** 12
e 12 **f** 11

Page 31: Factors

1 **a** 1, 2, 3, 4, 6, 12
   b 1, 2, 4, 8, 16
   c 1, 2, 3, 4, 6, 8, 12, 24
   d 1, 2, 3, 5, 6, 10, 15, 30
   e 1, 2, 3, 4, 6, 9, 12, 18, 36
   f 1, 2, 3, 6, 7, 14, 21, 42

2 **a** 200   **b** 90   **c** 300
   d 420   **e** 480   **f** 480
   g 600   **h** 420   **i** 720

Page 32: Square numbers

1 **a** 4   **b** 25
   c 100   **d** 16
   e 64   **f** 49

2 $9^2 = 9 \times 9 = 81$
   $4^2 = 4 \times 4 = 16$
   $11^2 = 11 \times 11 = 121$
   $7^2 = 7 \times 7 = 49$
   $12^2 = 12 \times 12 = 144$
   $8^2 = 8 \times 8 = 64$
   $6^2 = 6 \times 6 = 36$

Page 33: Cube numbers

1 $10^3 = 10 \times 10 \times 10 = 1000$
   $4^3 = 4 \times 4 \times 4 = 64$
   $3^3 = 3 \times 3 \times 3 = 27$
   $2^3 = 2 \times 2 \times 2 = 8$
   $1^3 = 1 \times 1 \times 1 = 1$
   $5^3 = 5 \times 5 \times 5 = 125$
   $6^3 = 6 \times 6 \times 6 = 216$

2 **a** 1   **b** 3
   c 6   **d** 1000
   e 8000   **f** 27 000

3 **a** 343   **b** 729

Page 34: Distributive law

1 **a** 40 + 64 = 104
   b 63 + 35 = 98
   c 180 + 24 = 204

2 **a** 112 cm²   **b** 162 cm²

Page 35: Column and short multiplication

1 **a** 2315   **b** 2108   **c** 2916

2 **a** 2241   **b** 2348   **c** 2382

Page 36: Short multiplication 2

1 **a** 25 371   **b** 14 748   **c** 31 816

2 **a** 23 115   **b** 15 816   **c** 16 744
   d 7416   **e** 43 253   **f** 58 976

Page 37: Written division

1 **a** 27   **b** 23   **c** 21
   d 63   **e** 47   **f** 57

2 **a** 37   **b** 31   **c** 24
   d 73   **e** 82   **f** 87

Page 38: Short division 1

1 **a** 3214   **b** 2131
   c 1215   **d** 2499
   e 1133   **f** 1242
   g 1434   **h** 3087

Page 39: Using rounding and inverses to check

1 **a** 200 × 6 = 1200   **2** **a** 1176
   b 800 ÷ 4 = 200   **b** 198
   c 600 ÷ 5 = 120   **c** 115
   d 200 × 8 = 1600   **d** 1488
   e 2000 × 3 = 6000   **e** 6084
   f 10 000 ÷ 4 = 2500   **f** 2398

3 Answers will vary.

Answers to Activities continued

Page 41: Short division 2

1 **a** 647 r3 **b** 489 r3
c 1075 r5 **d** 652 r2
e 910 r3 **f** 841 r1

2 **a** and **c**

Page 42: Remainders as fractions

1 **a** $1434\frac{1}{4}$
b $1337\frac{3}{7}$
c $847\frac{7}{9}$
d $1724\frac{4}{5}$

2 **a** $1434\frac{1}{2}$
b $833\frac{1}{4}$
c $756\frac{1}{2}$

3 **a** $566\frac{3}{4}$ **b** $322\frac{1}{2}$
c $456\frac{1}{3}$ **d** $815\frac{1}{2}$

Page 43: Rounding remainders up or down

1 **a** 13 **b** 8 **c** 8 **d** 7
e 8 **f** 13 **g** 6

Page 44: Scaling

1 14
2 36
3 48
4 56

Page 45: Grid multiplication

1 **a** 992 **b** 1935
c 2832 **d** 3773
e 5056 **f** 6714
g 10 536 **h** 18 140
i 34 374 **j** 43 995

Page 46: Grid and long multiplication

1 **a** 5797 **b** 14 496 **c** 23 220
d 20 634 **e** 17 974 **f** 32 562

2 **a** 7848 **b** 19 866
c 30 128 **d** 37 062
e 385 296 **f** 847 295

Page 47: Remainders as decimals

1 **a** 566.5 **b** 734.25
c 1075.75 **d** 852.4
e 810.75 **f** 1571.4

2 **a** $134\frac{1}{4}$ = 134.25
b $532\frac{3}{4}$ = 532.75

Page 48: Division word problems

1 **a** 1.25 litres **b** $1\frac{1}{5}$
c 1.5m **d** 14
e £7.50 **f** 16

Page 49: Long division 1

1 **a** 41 r2 **b** 85 r2
c 22 r1 **d** 71 r4

Page 50: Long division 2

1 **a** 377 r8 **b** 244 r9
c 270 r3 **d** 654 r9

Page 51: Multiplying and dividing by 10 and 100

1 **a** 460 **b** 54.3
c 26 **d** 48
e 4670 **f** 1230

2 **a** 0.2 **b** 4.8
c 0.54 **d** 0.5
e 0.321 **f** 0.49

Answers to Activities continued

Page 52: Multiplying decimals

1   **a** 39.2   **b** 39   **c** 49.8

     d 25.8   **e** 42.28   **f** 19.12

2   **a** 15.6   **b** 15.552   **c** 35.796

     d 38.661   **e** 55.366   **f** 70.512

Page 53: Dividing decimals

1   **a** 2.9   **b** 2.6   **c** 3.1

     d 1.46   **e** 1.97   **f** 1.08

     g 9.3   **h** 0.86   **i** 0.84

     j 6.98   **k** 1.36   **l** 23.5

1.36	2.4	3.87	1.9	4.82	3.6
23.5	4.04	9.27	3.1	1.46	9.3
2.9	0.84	2.6	6.98	8.1	0.86
8.3	7.56	4.9	3.7	8.64	1.97
2.7	0.46	6.2	4.86	3.9	1.08

Page 55: Mixed operations

1   **a** £12   **b** £0.60 or 60p

     c £1038   **d** £2.75

     e £2749

Page 56: Order of operations and brackets

1   **a** 17   **b** 62

     c 0   **d** 12

     e 10   **f** 17

2   **a** 13, 5   **b** 9, 6

     c 13, 1   **d** 16, 24

     e 7, 6   **f** 15, 13

Answers to Progress tests

PROGRESS TEST 1 – Page 13

1   4

2   **a** 21   **b** 20   **c** 12
    d 110   **e** 18   **f** 25
    g 24   **h** 36   **i** 60

3   3, 6, 9, 12, 15, 18, 21, 24, 27, 30, 33, 36

4   **a** 3   **b** 6   **c** 7
    d 10   **e** 7   **f** 6
    g 9   **h** 12   **i** 7

5   **a** $7 \times 5 = 35$
    b $50 \div 10 = 5$
    c $4 \times 7 = 28$

6   **a** £27   **b** 6

PROGRESS TEST 2 – Page 24

1   **a** 52   **b** 64   **c** 104
    d 18   **e** 27   **f** 7

2   **a** 280   **b** 5370   **c** 20430
    d 3080   **e** 4620   **f** 12040

3   **a** 1600   **b** 38600   **c** 403700
    d 8000   **e** 40600   **f** 320000

4   **a** 7   **b** 9   **c** 30
    d 64   **e** 238   **f** 510

5   **a** 6   **b** 8   **c** 13
    d 70   **e** 318   **f** 890

6   **a** 81   **b** 42   **c** 54
    d 24   **e** 48   **f** 72

7   **a** 6   **b** 5   **c** 7
    d 8   **e** 9   **f** 7

PROGRESS TEST 3 – Page 40

1   **a** 448   **b** 222   **c** 390
    d 333   **e** 264   **f** 608

2   **a** 12   **b** 7
    c 13   **d** 12

3   25, 9, 4, 36, 100, 81

4   27, 8, 1, 1000

5   **a** 50742   **b** 18435   **c** 27846

6   **a** 2114   **b** 2382

PROGRESS TEST 4 – Page 54

1   **a** 974 r4   **b** 606 r1

2   **a** $841\frac{3}{4}$ **b** $989\frac{1}{2}$

3   **a** 28125   **b** 4860   **c** 46104

4   **a** 1721.2   **b** 407.75

5   **a** 14   **b** 254.7
    c 24.854   **d** 3.65
    e 36.125   **f** 7.231

6   **a** 412 r2   **b** 161 r3

Answers to Final test

FINAL TEST – Pages 57–60

1   **a** 9   **b** 54   **c** 42

2   **a** 56   **b** 63
    c 40   **d** 49
    e 48   **f** 45
    g 28   **h** 27

3   **a** 360   **b** 450
    c 350   **d** 2300

4   **a** 290   **b** 6080   **c** 91270

5   **a** 2400   **b** 53600   **c** 826700

6   **a** 73   **b** 169   **c** 300

7   **a** 62   **b** 73   **c** 860

8   **a** 9 r3   **b** 9 r5   **c** 7 r1

9   **a** 1, 2, 4, 8, 16, 32
    b 1, 2, 3, 4, 6, 8, 9, 12, 18, 24, 36, 72

10   **a** 300   **b** 630

11   **a** 2860   **b** 61434

12   **a** 42282   **b** 285300

13   **a** 94   **b** 96

14   **a** 31.6   **b** 22.724

15   **a** 5.8   **b** 0.76

16   280

17   **a** 1   **b** 5
    c 3   **d** 343
    e 100   **f** 8

18   **a** 60p or £0.60   **b** $1\frac{2}{5}$

19   **a** $795\frac{3}{4}$ **b** $1305\frac{1}{2}$

20   **a** 35604   **b** 28810   **c** 45091

21   **a** 26   **b** 48

22   **a** 925.2   **b** 283.75

23   **a** $411\frac{4}{11}$ **b** $630\frac{3}{4}$